£4.99
UK only

CONTENTS

Published in Great Britain by World International, an imprint of Egmont Publishing Ltd., Egmont House, P.O. Box 111, Great Ducie Street, Manchester M60 3BL.

Printed in Italy.

ISBN 0-7498-2032-2

Garfield
ANNUAL

Created by
JiM DAVIS
Written by
Gordon Volke

WORLD INTERNATIONAL

Jon On Garfield

What would I have if I didn't have Garfield?

Houseplants, decent furniture, a full fridge, my sanity . . .

Things That Go Burp in the Night

"I don't get it," grumbled Garfield, rolling out of bed in the middle of the night. "I had supper, a mid evening snack, a late evening snack, a midnight feast and a final nightcap, but I'm still hungry. I'd better wake Jon to get me an early breakfast."

Garfield fetched a trumpet and a pair of cymbals from the toy cupboard. Then he kicked Odie upstairs to Jon's bedroom.

"If I can't sleep, Odie," he said, "neither can you."

Garfield sat Odie on one side of Jon's bed and positioned himself on the other.

"Wait for countdown, Odie," he explained, "and then we'll go into launch routine. Ten . . .nine . . .eight . . ."

Garfield had got right down to zero and was about to blast Jon three feet into the air with the trumpet when there was an ear-splitting CRASH outside. Jon sat bolt upright, knocking Garfield and Odie head-over-heels on to the floor.

"There's s-s-something outside," whispered Jon, tiptoeing fearfully to the window. "Maybe it's a poltergeist or a desperate vampire seeking a victim before dawn." With a trembling hand, Jon pulled aside the curtain. "Actually, the dustbin's fallen over!" he laughed.

Garfield had visions of Jon getting back into bed and going to sleep again, so he assumed a terrified expression and trod on Odie's tail, making the dog yowl pitifully.

"Gee, I'm sorry, boys!" cried Jon. "You must have been scared stiff by those noises outside.

That's why you came up to see me. Let's go down to the kitchen and find you something to eat. Then you can go back to sleep.''

"I've raised deceit into an art form," chuckled Garfield.

Odie had a glass of milk and some biscuits, and curled up in a corner of the kitchen. Garfield had 45 glasses of milk, 20 packets of biscuits, 12 bars of chocolate (family size), 5 microwave burgers and a giant pepperoni pizza — and begged for more!

"I need a club sandwich," he burped, pointing to the fridge, "and I should just about last until first light."

"Help yourself, Garfield," sighed Jon, wearily. "I'm going back to bed."

Garfield made himself a huge multi-decker sandwich with every sort of filling imaginable. He placed it on the window sill as he cranked his jaw open to swallow it.

"Thanks very much!" said a voice, as the window slid up and the sandwich disappeared through it.

Garfield stared, wide-eyed with disbelief. Then he dived head-first under the kitchen table.

"Spooks!" he wailed.

After a while, Garfield returned to his senses.

"Ghosts don't eat salami with cheese and pickle!" he exclaimed. "They like fried ectoplasm and stuff like that."

Marching outside, Garfield found a large fox sitting on the back doorsteps, picking his teeth.

"How do!" said the fox.

"And who, pray, are you?" inquired Garfield.

"Lionel's the name," replied the fox. "I like to steer clear of Reynard and all that sort of traditional stuff. I'm a modern, urban fox."

"Well, Lionel, it's been nice meeting you," said Garfield, starting to push the visitor down the path.

"Hold on a minute, lardball," protested the fox. "This is where I live."

"Since when?" asked Garfield.

"Since I knocked your dustbin over!" exclaimed Lionel. "There's more food in your house than in all the other houses put together."

"So you intend to stay here, eh?" said Garfield.

"Got it in one, buddy-boy," grinned Lionel.

"We'll see about that!" hissed Garfield.

Garfield marched indoors and fetched his trumpet.

"If I blow this," he thought, "Fox Face will think the hunt is coming. He'll be off like a shot!" Garfield held the back gate open and gave a series of toots. But instead of seeing Lionel whiz past him, the fox sauntered over, rummaging in his bag.

"You play a cool horn, man," he chuckled. "Lemme find my sax and we can do a duet."

"Sorry, pal," growled Garfield, "the only tune I know is 'Hit The Road, Jack'!"

Lionel went back to eating Garfield's sandwich and finished it with a satisfied burp.

"That should hold me until first light," he grinned.

"This guy even pinches my lines!" snorted Garfield, marching indoors again. He returned carrying a large cake. "Have a slice for dessert, Lionel," he called. "I've made it especially for you." Garfield had iced the cake with a mixture of black pepper, chilli powder and vindaloo curry paste. His plan was that Lionel should eat a few mouthfuls and become a fox-shaped blowtorch!

"Don't mind if I do," chuckled Lionel, cramming a whole slice in his mouth. He chomped it up with obvious relish and reached for another . . . and another.

"What's wrong here?" thought Garfield, sampling the cake himself. "Did I use the wrong spices! GAAHGH! N-N-No I didn't!"

Clutching his smoking throat, Garfield raced round the garden. He drank from the birdbath, the fishpond and the water butt before lying down with the hose squirting into his mouth.

"Meant to tell you," said Lionel, casually. "I lived at an Indian take-away before I moved here. My taste-buds are completely shock-proof."

"Mine have just left the country!" gasped Garfield.

Realising Lionel could be there to stay, Garfield decided to risk everything on an all-or-nothing gamble.

"Foxes are supposed to be cunning," he said. "So are we cats. Let's have a contest to see who's cleverer. Winner takes all."

"You're on!" agreed Lionel.

Garfield racked his brains for a way to fool the fox. Then he remembered, in the best stories, they always asked three riddles.

"What's full of holes but can hold water?" he cried.

"A sponge!" replied Lionel, instantly. "Next?"

"What driver can't drive?" asked Garfield.

"Screwdriver!" snapped the fox. "Last one, please!"

"What bow can't be . . ." began Garfield.

"A rainbow can't be tied!" cried Lionel, answering the riddle even before Garfield had finished asking it. "Now it's my turn. What runs round the garden without moving?"

"That's easy," laughed Garfield. "The path."

"WRONG!" whooped Lionel. "It's the fence. The path runs down the middle."

"That's *this* garden . . .!" protested Garfield.

"You should have checked that before you answered, shouldn't you!" retorted Lionel.

"That's not fair!" cried Garfield.

"All's fair in love and riddles," chortled Lionel, tossing his bag into Garfield's arms. "Kindly show me round, my man!"

Garfield gave Lionel a guided tour of the house. The fox showed most interest in Jon's bunny slippers, Garfield's rubber chicken, Stretch, and the mice (who dived into their mouseholes and waved white flags.) Finally, the newcomer returned to the kitchen. Odie had just awakened and was having a stretch.

"What's that slobbery thing?" asked Lionel.

"That's Odie," replied Garfield.

"I didn't ask *who*," said Lionel, "I asked *what*."

"Odie's a dog," explained Garfield. "A four-footed canine — just like you!"

Lionel looked aghast. He snatched his bag back from Garfield.

"I'm leaving!" he cried, bolting for the door. "You can't link me with a bonebrain like that. Think of my street cred — not to mention my country cred!"

"Nice one, Odie," chuckled Garfield. "As a special reward, I won't kick you again today."

The crisis over, Garfield suddenly felt very tired. He flopped into his bed and fell fast asleep. Soon he was dreaming of a pizza the size of a moon crater that floated tantalisingly in front of him. Garfield got up in his sleep and started following his dream meal round the kitchen.

Meanwhile, upstairs, Jon was just starting to stir. Suddenly, there was another loud CRASH from below.

"Not again!" cried Jon, leaping out of bed.

Jon raced downstairs and turned on the kitchen light, revealing Garfield blundering round the kitchen like a zombie.

"So it was YOU all along, Garfield!" cried Jon. "Well, you're not going to disturb any more nights through your greediness. From now on, I'm padlocking the larder and the fridge — and the dustbin. How do you feel about that?"

"Foxed!" groaned Garfield.

BIRD BATH
BLUES

LASAGNE AND THE WORLD LASAGNES WITH YOU...

...DIET AND YOU DIET ALONE!

Garfield's

BELIEVE IT
OR DON'T

Here are ten amazing facts. Six of them are completely true; the other four, to quote Garfield, are "a load of baloney" (and he should know — he's eaten several loads in his time!) Can you pick out the imposters? (Answers opposite)

1 Tiger, Tiger, Burping Bright

An Indian tigress killed and ate over 430 people before being caught in 1907.

2 My Word

The longest word in English is FLOCCIPAUCINIHILIPILIFICATION which means "to estimate something to be worthless." The word has 29 letters and was used by the famous English novelist, Sir Walter Scott.

3 Dog Tired

On a cold night, Australian aborigines used to sleep with their dogs covering them as blankets. This has given rise to the phrase "a five dog night" meaning "bitterly cold."

4 It's All Greek To Me!

Like Garfield, the Greek Philosopher Plato cannot have been very good at getting up in the mornings. He invented an 'alarm clock' which consisted of three containers set at different levels. Water dripped from one to the other and eventually forced air out of a narrow tube, emitting a loud whistle.

5 Prehistoric Pooch

Scientists in Indiana, USA, have recently discovered the remains of a small, dog-like dinosaur which they have named *Megaslobberodiesaurus*. Related to the *Diplodocus*, which had a brain the size of a walnut, this creature is thought to have a brain the size of a pea.

6 Astounding Feet

Flying frogs on the island of Java in the East Indies have developed webbed feet that enable them to hover in the air and pounce on unsuspecting insects passing underneath.

7 Bows Of Burning Gold

In 1971, an American archer called Harry Drake fired an arrow from a footbow that travelled over 1,850 metres (that's well over a mile.) In 1988, he beat his own record by firing a crossbow arrow a distance of 1,870 metres!

8 My Giddy Aunt!

The world record for riding on a children's roundabout is held by a 62 year old widow, Mrs Mary Hutchins. In June, 1981, this amazing lady completed 127,561 continuous revolutions, propelled by her three sons and two daughters. The epic circular journey took 3 days, 7 hours and 24 minutes.

9 All Present And Correct, Sir!

In September 1928, a sailing ship left Germany, bound for Brazil in South America. The journey took nearly five months and, during the course of it, 47 passengers died. But, at the same time, 47 children were born on board ship — so it arrived with exactly the same number of passengers with which it departed.

10 A Spanner In The Works

In October 1934, Big Ben failed to strike for a total of 19 days, the longest stoppage ever recorded — even including the Blitz during World War II. The fault was finally located in a small corner of the clock's huge mechanism. Workmen, who had serviced the clock the previous summer, had left a spanner which had fallen down and jammed two cogs.

Answers

The following facts are false: 5, 6, 8 and 10

Garfield on Pooky

A cat without a teddy is like
a pizza without pepperoni!

REMEMBER:
Garfield can speak directly to other animals, but not to humans. He only comments on what humans say and they cannot hear his comments.

A GEEK IN POLITICS

(Read for fun or act out with your friends)

SPEAKING PARTS:
GARFIELD, JON, LIZ and ARLENE
BARKING PART: ODIE

SCENE 1. JON'S BEDROOM

Late at night. Garfield is dozing on Jon's bed. Jon enters, holding his toothbrush and looking thoughtful.

JON: If Clint Eastwood can do it, so can I!

GARFIELD: ZZZZZZZ!

JON: Wake up, Garfield, I reckon I should follow in Clint Eastwood's footsteps. What do you say?

GARFIELD: Go ahead, punk, make my supper!

JON (GETTING READY FOR BED): Imagine it, Garfield, ME — Mayor of the town.

GARFIELD: Yeah, imagine!

JON: Do you think I'll get elected?

GARFIELD: Anyone who takes his trousers off as if he's treading grapes would certainly get my vote!

SCENE 2. THE STREET

The following day. Garfield and Arlene are out delivering Jon's election leaflets.

ARLENE: I can't believe Jon sat up all night writing this stuff!

GARFIELD: It's amazing. Listen! (READS) 'When I'm Mayor, I'll make all government officials wear tartan trousers, plaid jackets and luminous ties. Also, I intend to organise big prize sock-sorting competitions for all.'

ARLENE: How many leaflets left?
GARFIELD: Who cares! Slip me some lip!
ARLENE: Get off, Garfield. How many left!
GARFIELD: 4,327!
ARLENE: PHEW!
GARFIELD: When you sigh like that, a gale blows through the gap in your front teeth.
ARLENE: Button it, Garfield!
GARFIELD: No, keep sighing like a steam train, baby cakes. I'll shake out the sack.

Jon comes running up, waving urgently.

JON: HEY! Why are my leaflets blowing all over town?
GARFIELD (RAISING ONE ARM AND GRINNING): Air mail delivery!

SCENE 3. A TV STUDIO

Two days later. Jon waits nervously to appear on local television. Garfield and Odie are with him.

JON: How do I look?
GARFIELD: Like a cross between William Shakespeare and Binky the Clown.
JON: I knew this frilly shirt was a masterstroke. It makes me look so different.
GARFIELD: You can say that again!

Jon walks away, wagging his finger at Garfield and Odie

JON: Promise to behave yourselves while I'm on air?
ODIE (OBEDIENTLY): ARF!
GARFIELD: No we don't, sieve-brain! We're doing our routine, remember?
ODIE (EXCITEDLY): ARF, ARF!
GARFIELD: As your memory-span is about five seconds, I'd better remind you. When the cameras start rolling, we run in front of them and do our Torvill and Dean on roller boots. You have brought them, haven't you?
ODIE (NODDING): ARF!
GARFIELD (DREAMILY): We'll be sensational! Offers will flood in — national TV, Las Vegas, Broadway . . .
ODIE (URGENTLY): ARF, ARF, ARF!
GARFIELD: Wassamatter? Hey, they've started!

Garfield and Odie skate onto the set. Immediately, the floor manager picks them up by the scruff of the neck.

GARFIELD: Hoi, put me down, you big bully! Don't you know talent when you see it?

The official drops Garfield and Odie onto the pavement outside the studio.

GARFIELD: OWWCH!
ODIE: OOOFF!
GARFIELD: Huh! Who wants to be a superstar, anyway?

SCENE 4. JON'S HOUSE

A week later. Jon is on the phone to Liz.

JON: I'm very worried, Liz.
LIZ: You can't help having muscles that look like pimples.
JON: It's not that . . .
LIZ: Something wrong with Garfield?
JON: No, I haven't seen him for days. He's miffed because I haven't been around to feed him every five minutes.
LIZ: What's wrong, then?
JON: It's the election. A new candidate has entered the fray.
LIZ: That shouldn't worry you — you're not going to win anyway.
JON: Exactly! Listen to what this guy's promising: the abolition of the working week, pasta on prescription, free TV and junk food delivered to every house ten times a day for the next ten years.
LIZ: Who is he?
JON: Nobody knows. He's a mystery.
LIZ: Try to find out, will you? I'd like to vote for him!

SCENE 5. OUTSIDE THE TOWN HALL

Election day. Late in the evening. Voting is over and Liz, Arlene and Odie wait eagerly for the result. Eventually, Jon comes towards them down the steps, looking glum.

JON: I've never been so humiliated in all my life!
LIZ: Yes, you have. What about the time in the restaurant . . .?
JON: (CUTTING IN): Do you know how many votes I got?
ARLENE: NONE.
JON: NONE! And do you know who won it?
ODIE: ARF-ield! ARF-ield!
JON: GARFIELD! By a landslide majority!

Garfield appears on the steps, looking very pleased with himself.

GARFIELD: That's MAYOR Garfield to you, my man!
JON: This is ridiculous, Garfield. You can't possibly . . .
Garfield pushes everybody towards a huge, black limo that has drawn up outside the town hall.

GARFIELD: Jump in my stretch, you guys. And put on the funny hats. The outside caterers should be ready for us at home.
ARLENE: What's going on, Garfield?
GARFIELD: From now on, Jon's place is Party Headquarters — so LET'S PARTY!

BIRDBATH
BLUES 2

BZZZZ

JIM DAVIS   10-2

CLICK

PLAYING WITH MY ELECTRIC RAZOR, GARFIELD?

NEVER MIND

© 1986 United Feature Syndicate, Inc.

GARFIELD!   JIM DAVIS

© 1986 United Feature Syndicate, Inc.   10-3

YOU'RE USING MY TOOTHBRUSH!

STICK AROUND. YOU CAN WATCH ME FLOSS

IS NOTHING SACRED?!

WHERE'S THAT MOUTHWASH?

Z

© 1986 United Feature Syndicate, Inc.

CRASH! DONK!

WHAP!

THE MONDAY PAPER

JIM DAVIS 10-13

GARFIELD! YOU'RE NOT GOING TO BELIEVE THIS! I WAS IN A BAKERY TODAY BUYING A CAKE WHEN THREE MIDGETS IN GORILLA COSTUMES RACED IN, SET THE PLACE ON FIRE AND RAN OUT WITH THE CASH REGISTER!

WOW!

COME ON, JON. DON'T SPARE THE DETAILS!

© 1986 United Feature Syndicate, Inc.

CHOCOLATE OR VANILLA FROSTING?

JIM DAVIS 10-15

**THIS WAY ROUND,
I'M JUST INDIFFERENT!**

Arlene On Garfield

Going out with Garfield is like being a skittle — one minute you're getting bowled over, next minute you're being stood up!

MARK BUT THIS

FLEA

So wrote John Donne, the 17th Century English poet. Donne admired fleas. He felt they helped to unite him with his girlfriend by biting them both! Garfield is not so keen. As far as he's concerned, fleas are like Odie, Mondays and food commercials when he's on a diet — a terrible irritation!

Who's right? Decide for yourself by hopping over to the next two pages for some fascinating info about these little mites.(Aren't you *itching* to find out more about them?)

There are about 1,600 different types of flea around the world.

 All fleas are parasites. They cannot live on their own; they have to live on another animal.

 Fleas have specially adapted mouths which enable them to bite and suck the blood of their hosts. (This explains their scientific name *Siphonaptera* which means 'blood-sucking insect'.)

 Usually, fleas feed every day, but they are very hardy and can survive for several months without any food.

 Cat fleas, dog fleas and human fleas are all separate species and have differently shaped heads, but they don't stick exclusively to their main hosts. Cat fleas also infest dogs and man; dog fleas exist on cats and humans, and human fleas can live on a wide variety of mammals including pigs!

 Cat fleas reproduce at a phenomenal rate. An adult female sheds up to 20 eggs a day and produces about 500 eggs in a normal lifetime.

 Dog fleas have an unusual male/female size difference. The female can grow to 4mm long, but the male only reaches about 2mm.

Human fleas are very long-lived. In suitable conditions, an individual can survive for anything up to 18 months.

Big fleas have little fleas
On their backs to bite 'em,
Little fleas have smaller fleas -
And ad infinitum!

Traditional Rhyme

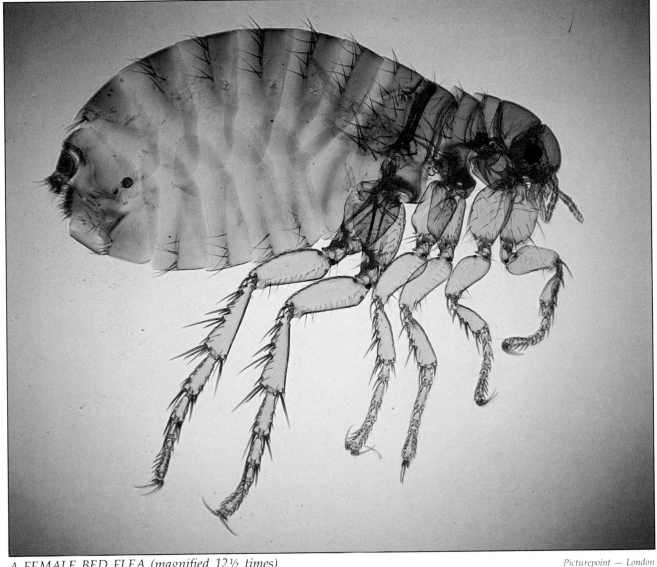

A FEMALE BED FLEA (magnified 12½ times)

Picturepoint — London

Most fleas are irritating and unpleasant pests, but rat fleas have a more sinister side. In the past, they have been responsible for transmitting bubonic plague. The Black Death of the Middle Ages and the Great Plague of the 1660s were caused by the bite of infected rat fleas.

Fleas have a special leathery skin which protects them from injury when their hosts scratch themselves.

Some fleas are very fussy about who they live with. The shrew flea, for example, will only live on shrews and no other type of rodent!

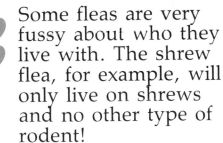
The most amazing thing about all fleas is their ability to jump. Given their tiny size, the height they can reach and the distance they can travel is truly astonishing. It has been estimated that, if a man had an equal jumping ability, he would travel approximately *five city blocks!*

27

LET'S FACE IT!

PARTY POOPER

OKAY, ODIE. TAKE THESE PARTY INVITATIONS AND PUT THEM IN THE MAILBOX

© 1986 United Feature Syndicate, Inc.

COME ON, GARFIELD. THE SOCIAL EVENT OF THE SEASON HAS ARRIVED

DING DONG

I WAS EXPECTING THE UPPER CRUST

AND YOU GOT THE CRUMBS

WHO TOLD ODIE
HE NEEDED TRAINING?

THERE'S NO TIME LIKE THE PAST

JON'S SARTORIAL ELEGANCE QUIZ

Questions about Clothes and Fashion

1. What were prehistoric clothes made of?
a) Animal skins
b) Cotton
c) Prehistoric denim

2. Edwardian women wore tight corsets to give them an ''hour glass figure.'' What were the corsets made of?
a) Lego
b) Whalebone
c) Bamboo

3. Roman togas were only worn by important people on special occasions. What did ordinary Romans wear?
a) Woollen cloaks
b) Tunics
c) Hotpants

4. Skirts were first worn around 3,000 B.C. by the ancient Sumerians of Mesopotamia.
a) True
b) False

5. Can you match these famous modern fashions with the decade in which they occurred?
Drainpipe trousers   1960s
Platform shoes   1980s
Mini skirts   1950s
Slashed jeans   1970s

6. The sewing machine, first used in the 1850s, caused a fashion revolution by allowing clothes to be mass-produced. Who invented it?
a) Rumpelstiltskin
b) Alexander Graham Bell
c) Isaac Merrit Singer

7. Can you complete this sentence?
American cowboys in the late 19th Century were the first people to wear - - - - -.

8. How did Teddy Boys of the 1950s get their name?
a) They carried teddy bears
b) They dressed in the style of American president, Teddy Roosevelt
c) They wore long jackets like Edwardian gentlemen

9. What is a ruff?
a) A frilly decoration worn round the neck
b) The first stages of a fashion design
c) The noise Odie makes when he barks

10. Which bathing fashion was introduced in 1946?
a) The bathing hut
b) The bathing hat
c) The bikini

11. What do these people have in common?
Naomi Campbell, Nikki Taylor, Kate Moss and Tyra Banks

12. Which of these materials is the odd one out?
Wool, silk, leather, nylon, cotton

13. What is a smoking cap?
a) Something you put in a toy gun
b) A decorated hat worn by Victorian gentlemen at home
c) A cap that catches fire

14. What type of fashion item did Elvis Presley sing about?
a) Jailhouse suits
b) Blue suede shoes
c) Hound dog collars

15. Which of these places is not a fashion centre?
a) Paris, France
b) London, England
c) Muncie, USA
d) New York, USA
e) Milan, Italy

16. Who would wear a kimino?
a) A Japanese lady
b) A Chinese lady
c) A dragon

17. A doublet and hose was a special jacket with a pipe down the sleeve worn by Medieval farmers when watering their crops.
a) True
b) False

18. Beau Brummel was a famous dandy and leader of fashion in the late 18th/early 19th Century. What does the name 'Beau' mean?
a) He wore a lot of bows
b) Handsome/very smart
c) His clothes took you by surprise

19. Who introduced the fashion of men wearing wigs in the 17th Century?
a) Judge Jeffries
b) The Laughing Cavalier
c) King Louis XIV of France

20. Jon is very fond of 'plaid' socks and ties. What is the other name for this pattern?
a) Tartan
b) Plain
c) Really geeky

Answers

1. a) Animal Skins
2. b) Whalebone
3. b) Tunics
4. a) True
5. Drainpipe trousers — 1950s. Platform shoes — 1970s. Mini skirts — 1960s. Slashed jeans — 1980s
6. c) Isaac Merrit Singer
7. Jeans
8. c) They wore long jackets like Edwardian gentlemen
9. a) A frilly decoration worn round the neck
10. c) The bikini
11. They are Supermodels (top fashion models)
12. Nylon. (It is man-made; the others are natural materials.)
13. b) A decorated hat worn by Victorian gentlemen at home
14. b) Blue suede shoes
15. c) Muncie, USA
16. a) A JapaneseLady
17. b) False. (Hose means leggings or tight trousers — as in the modern word "hosiery".)
18. b) Handsome/very smart
19. c) King Louis XIV of France.
20. a) Tartan

The Mailman
On Garfield

!!**!&*!!!**

ODIE'S FAVOURITE DOG STORY

Greyfriars Bobby

Edinburgh in the 1860s was a city of contrasts. The Scottish capital boasted many fine buildings inhabited by well-to-do folk with their servants, carriages and beautiful clothes. It also hosted some of the country's poorest citizens who eked out a miserable existence in filthy, overcrowded slums. One such area was Greyfriars, a jumble of grimy tenement buildings that huddled like a pile of old boxes at the foot of Edinburgh Castle.

Once a week, for as long as anyone could remember, Old Jock the shepherd had visited Greyfriars market. Jock was a hired hand who worked on the sheep farms in the surrounding hills. Seventy years of rain, wind and sun gave Old Jock the appearance of a gnarled tree. Up until recently, he had always been alone, but now he was accompanied by a young Skye terrier called Bobby. The little dog belonged to Farmer Caird, but he had befriended Old Jock and went everywhere with him. They made a comical pair, the old shepherd slow and deliberate in everything he did, the lively terrier bursting with energy and full of mischief.

One November morning, as they approached the bustling market, Bobby spied a cat sitting on the wall of Greyfriars churchyard. The cat hissed and spat, and Bobby could not resist the challenge. With a joyful yelp, the terrier chased the cat under the big, wooden gates. ''Come out of there!'' yelled Mr Brown, the church caretaker. A chase ensued, in which Bobby sped after the cat and Mr Brown and Old Jock lumbered after Bobby, round and round the churchyard. Eventually, the cat dived under a tombstone and Bobby was caught.

''Animals are strictly forbidden in the church grounds,'' scolded Mr Brown.

''Bobby will never set foot in here again,'' promised Old Jock.

As the winter drew on, Bobby noticed that his beloved master was getting slower and slower. The old shepherd also had a cough, a persistent, rasping cough that got worse every night and prevented them both from sleeping. One day, when the snow lay deep on the ground and icicles hung like glittering swords from the roofs of the houses, Old Jock developed a fever. He stumbled into Mr Trail's eating-house, where he had eaten his dinner for the last fifty years, sweating like a labourer in mid-summer.

''Let me take you to the hospital,'' said Mr Trail.

''I'll have nothing to do with hospitals,'' roared Old Jock. ''They're for people who are old and sick!''

That night, Old Jock died. Bobby was by his side, licking and nuzzling his grey hand in a vain attempt to wake his master. A few days later, Bobby followed the funeral procession to Greyfriars churchyard and stood by the gate in the freezing afternoon rain, watching Old Jock being buried. Then, when everyone had gone and the churchyard was silent, Bobby slipped inside and lay on the stone that marked Jock's grave.

He stayed there all night, braving the bitter wind and terrifying darkness. Mr Brown noticed him the following morning, huddling on the fresh white tombstone.

''You again!'' roared the caretaker. ''Be off with you!''

Mr Brown chased Bobby through the gate, but the dog doubled back and entered the churchyard again through a hole in the wall. The caretaker had hardly got his breath back when he found Bobby sitting on the grave again.

''Out!'' he yelled. ''OUT, OUT, OUT!''

Mr Brown spent all morning trying to chase Bobby away. Every time he got the dog out, Bobby found some way to return. In the end, Mr Brown gave up and caught the terrier instead.

''I'll hand you over to Mr Trail,'' he said.

The plan did not work. Bobby spent all afternoon whining and scratching at the door of Mr Trail's eating-house. And, whenever the door was opened, the dog sped out and raced back to Old Jock's grave.

''I can't let him stay there,'' explained Mr Brown. ''The elders of the church have told me that animals must not be allowed to spoil the graves. I will lose my job as sure as Victoria is our Queen.''

A few days later, a cart drew up at the churchyard gates. Mr Brown was driving it and Mr Trail sat in the back with a sturdy wooden box. The two men crept up to Bobby, still keeping his vigil for Old Jock, and put him in the box.

''Settle down, Bobby,'' soothed Mr Trail, ''it's a very long ride to Mr Caird's farm.'' They drove up into the hills. The sheep farmer was pleased to have his little dog back.

''My barn's full of rats,'' he said, ''and terriers like Bobby are good at catching them.'' So, with a final ruffle of his shaggy coat, Mr Brown and Mr Trail left Bobby to his new job in his rightful home.

Imagine their surprise, when a few days later, the two men found Bobby sitting on Old

Jock's tombstone again!

"The wee critter must have run away and made his way back here," exclaimed Mr Trail.

"Amazing!" gasped Mr Brown. "All that way through unfamiliar countryside and busy city streets!"

The landlord and the caretaker did not know what to do next. But Mr Brown's daughter, Jennie, did.

"Let Bobby stay!" she cried.

"But the church elders . . ." protested her father.

"Speak to them," exclaimed Jennie. "Explain what's happened. Are their hearts so hard that their rules cannot be broken for once?"

A meeting was held and it was agreed that Bobby — but no other animal — should be allowed to remain in the churchyard. He would be fed and looked after by Jennie Brown. And so Bobby became known as Greyfriars Bobby and his fame spread throughout the city. The citizens of Edinburgh, rich and poor, came to see Bobby and play with the friendly terrier. But, every evening, when the crowds had gone, Bobby resumed his lonely vigil on Old Jock's tombstone.

The years passed and, like his master before him, Bobby began to feel the effects of the harsh Scottish weather. His muzzle grew grey and he could no longer run as fast or jump as high. One autumn evening, Jennie — now a grown woman — brought Bobby's supper and noticed that the little dog was not moving.

"You'll not be needing this," she said, putting the dish aside.

They buried Bobby beside Old Jock and put up a bronze plaque to his memory.

"If only people had as much love for each other as Bobby had for Old Jock," sighed Jennie, "the world would be a much happier place."

SAY CHEESE

SPINACH IS FOR THE SAILORMEN ...

**...AND RAISINS ARE
FOR HEALTH FREAKS!**

Odie On Love, Truth and
The Meaning Of Life!

ARF!

BINKY

AND HIS BROTHERS

The Lowdown on Clowns

Garfield's friend, Binky the Clown, belongs to a profession that's as old as civilisation itself. Every age and culture has enjoyed the antics of fools and funnymen whose job has been to make people laugh. This is their story. *Bring on the clowns!*

The Pharaohs of Ancient Egypt were entertained by clowns. They were African pigmies called *dangas* and we know of their existence from Egyptian stone carvings. The Ancient Greeks also had clowns. They were called *parasites* and wandered from place to place, performing for anyone who would employ them. The Romans had two types of clown. One, known as the *cicirrus*, performed at public games dressed up as a bird. The other, the *stupidus*, appeared in the theatre where they made fun of the characters and mimicked the action of the play.

The tradition of the Roman cicirrus was continued by the Medieval *jester*. These clowns wore a long cap with a bell on the end and carried a stick called a marotte with a puppet on the end. Some worked in the royal courts of Europe, amusing the King and often dispensing wise advice; others worked at the many fairs that were the main source of entertainment at the time.

By Elizabethan times in England, another type of clown had evolved — the *bessy*. This was often a man dressed up in women's clothes who played the fool in morris dances and during plays put on by wandering performers called mummers.

Also during the 16th Century, the clown came to the theatre. This development began in Italy with a famous theatrical company called the Commedia dell' Arte. They invented three types of clown that are still seen today — *Harlequin*, a white-faced clown in a colourful costume who is an astonishing acrobat; *Pierrot*, a sad-faced clown who wears a white outfit with pom-poms, and *Pulcinello*, a bad-tempered clown with a hook nose who has become Mr Punch in Punch and Judy puppet shows.

The greatest clown of all time was born in London in 1779. His name was *Joey Grimaldi* and he made his first peformance as a baby clown at the age of two. His father was a cruel man who beat his son if he found him laughing, so Joey became skilled at pretending to cry when his father was around and laughing again when he was gone. This became the basis of his act — appearing to be sad, but really being happy and mischievous. Grimaldi was also very creative and invented a number of clowning tricks that are still performed today. Modern circus clowns are often called ''Joeys'' and their act is called a ''Grimaldi act''.

After Grimaldi, clowns became less popular in the theatre, but they found a new home — the circus. Circuses did not exist until the mid 18th Century. They were

invented by Philip Astley, an ex-soldier and skilled horseman who put on shows at his riding school in London. Astley invited acrobats, tightrope walkers and strongmen to join his team of performing horses, and then added a clown, *Mr Merryman*. The phenomenal success of Astley's show led to the establishment of circuses all over Europe and in America.

The type of circus clown most often seen today is called an *Auguste*. He wears big, baggy trousers and huge shoes which look ridiculous and cause a lot of comic accidents. The character was invented by *Tom Belling*, an American acrobat working at a circus in Germany. (The word "Auguste" means "clumsy fool" in German.) To make his character even funnier, Belling added a puzzled look, as if he could not understand why everything kept going wrong. This combination of total disaster and childlike innocence is still the hallmark of the Auguste clown.

Since Belling's day, there have been many famous circus clowns, but two have become household names. *Grock* was an Auguste who wore a huge, ill-fitting overcoat and boots so big he could hardly walk in them. His act involved trying — usually unsuccessfully — to play the piano or violin. *Coco*, another Auguste who wore an enormous check suit, was famous for drenching his fellow performers with buckets of water. Coco's trademark, a false red nose, has become the symbol of modern-day Comic Relief.

Finally, no history of the clown would be complete without mention of *Charlie Chaplin*. His "little tramp" character with his flat-footed walk and badly-fitting clothes delighted a worldwide audience of hundreds of millions thanks to the invention of film. In his silent comedies such as The Kid (1921) and The Gold Rush (1925), he played a lowly, pathetic figure causing chaos wherever he went. Chaplin was the ultimate clown.

Charlie Chaplin as "the little tramp"

Picturepoint — London

EARTH, AIR, FIRE and LASAGNE
Garfield's Astrological Birth Chart

Garfield was born on June 19th, 1978, in Indiana, USA. (That's where Jim Davis drew the first Garfield strip and had it published in 41 American newspapers.) So Garfield's astrological birth chart looks like this —

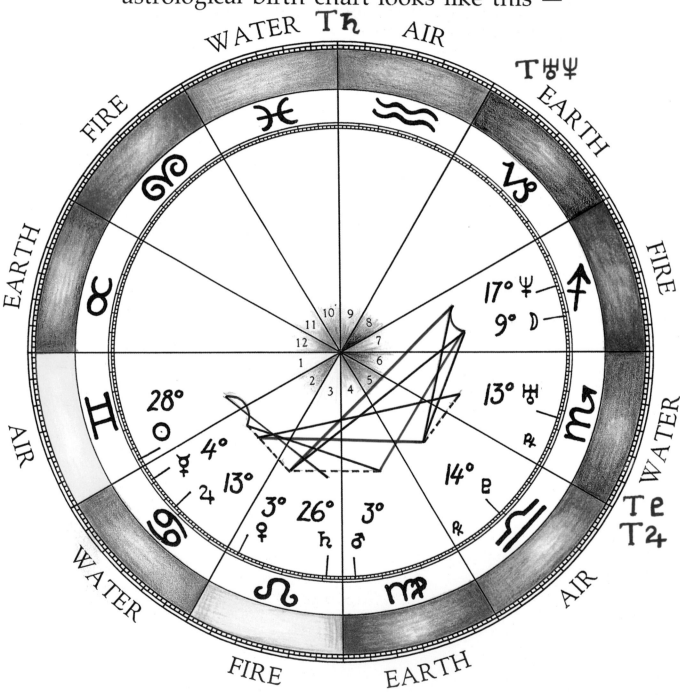

48

The Stars On A Superstar

The chart shows the pattern of Garfield's stars. This is what the stars tell us about Garfield . . .

The overall impression of Garfield's character is one of self-interest. Garfield's Sun shines brightly in Gemini in his first house, which means he stamps his personality firmly onto everything around him. By nature he is inquisitive, fickle, sociable and young at heart.

The Sagittarius side of him is a bit of a wanderer, but with the Moon alongside Neptune, he is always happy to return to his own backyard. (He really prefers to be an armchair traveller.)

Mars is about energy and it's fair to say that Garfield hates living in a mess (although he has no objection to causing it) and will put his somewhat limited energies into ensuring that the fridge is cleaned out, that his own personal stuff is left untouched, that he is well-groomed and that he gets the best of everything. His critical eye is often offended by Jon's appalling taste, yet another side of Garfield adores bright, colourful things and showing off.

Garfield's pride, vanity and sense of drama come from Leo (king of cats) which is in his third house of communication. Leo is also interacting with Sagittarius, giving a 'show-biz' feel and explaining Garfield's love of an appreciative audience and his mirror.

Pluto, the most distant planet in our solar system, rules over secrets, power and control. Pluto also happens to be King of the Underworld and a very large dog. Garfield has Pluto in house number five, his playbox. It is easy to see the connection with Odie, the dog he plays with when he is not dominating him or booting him off the table!

Garfield's chart-ruler and thinking planet, Mercury, is in a comfort-seeking watery 'this-is-my-place' mood. Taken in conjunction with dominating elements of earth and fire, it is little wonder that Garfield is a great home-lover for whom all creature-comforts are very important.

Finally, Cancer is alongside Jupiter in the second house of natural talents, resources and possessions. This is where we grow to fulfilment. In Garfield's case, this centres on the acquisition of food into which he puts an incredible amount of energy and imagination. He always wants more, and usually gets it!

What Does The Future Hold?

Based on current planetary movements in relation to Garfield's birthchart, it is possible to predict that Garfield will continue to enjoy great success and popularity. There is a suggestion that something unexpected will come into his life, but it is not clear exactly what. Garfield will also present us with new aspects of himself in 1995, but he will never lose his sense of humour or love of mischief.

Chart and information kindly supplied by **Alison Condie**, *Chairman of the Scottish Astrological Association.*

PUZZLE PARADE

THE GREAT ANAGRAM SCAM

The letters of the words in the left-hand column can be rearranged to make new words in the right-hand column. There is a special double clue to help you find both words and the first pair have been done as an example. (Answers opposite)

BUT — Objection to a bath — TUB

– – – – – Rodents in the sky – – – – –

– – – Underwater transport in the highstreet – – –

– – – – – Knocked out by Brazils and pistachios – – – – –

– – – – – – Sporting groups that come to the boil – – – – – –

– – – – – Feeling miserable in verse – – – – –

– – – – – – Light beer fit for a king – – – – – –

– – – – – – Theft of the most unimportant – – – – – –

– – – – – Somewhere to sit in a certain direction – – – – –

– – – – – – – Unsafe at the front and the back of the house – – – – – – –

GARFIELD'S GRAFFITI GAME

Three letters are missing from each alphabet box and a single digit number from the number box. Find the missing letters and number and write them in the spaces below to make a message Garfield scrawled on the wall. (Answers opposite)

E	R		B
	F	H	V
G		Q	K
	I	U	D
P		L	V
	Z	T	S
A		M	C
	Y	X	W

25		9	1
	5	23	8
24		6	16
	17	18	11
12		22	13
	26	7	10
14		19	3
2	20	15	21

A		S	G
	T	E	J
F		U	H
	R	K	V	B
C		P		W
	X	D	M
Q		N		Y
		O	

– – – – – – – – – – – – – – – –

WIT & WISDOM WORD SEARCH

Can you find ten of Garfield's favourite sayings hidden in the grid? They are spelt in all directions including backwards and each section of every saying is in a different place. The first one has been done as an example. (Solution below)

P	B	X	N	A	R	S	I	G	N	I	D	A	E	R
N	E	V	E	R	T	R	U	S	T	L	V	G	T	B
W	S	N	Z	T	E	D	D	Y	B	E	A	R	U	C
O	T	A	C	G	N	I	L	I	M	S	A	Y	C	F
R	F	J	I	B	R	E	A	K	Y	E	V	A	H	M
U	R	B	I	G	F	A	T	A	T	N	S	Y	A	O
O	I	O	F	M	P	I	S	A	Q	T	T	L	I	R
Y	E	R	O	M	Z	I	H	P	C	H	B	Y	R	F
E	N	E	S	L	Y	I	S	A	F	E	Y	A	Y	D
B	D	D	Q	K	D	L	S	Y	T	P	N	D	D	E
R	Q	B	O	Y	C	M	I	N	A	E	M	O	E	V
L	U	O	A	G	A	O	R	F	T	D	Z	T	A	L
B	P	R	X	P	S	L	R	R	E	T	N	G	L	O
O	R	E	M	M	U	S	R	O	F	H	J	O	T	V
M	D	D	N	D	E	R	O	B	M	I	R	D	M	E

1. BIG FAT / HAIRY DEAL
2. I HATE / MONDAYS
3. I HATE / CUTE
4. ROCKS / EVOLVED FROM / DOGS
5. I BREAK / FOR SUMMER
6. I'M BORED / BORED BORED
7. BE YOUR OWN / BEST FRIEND
8. NEVER TRUST / A SMILING CAT
9. READING IS / MY LIFE
10. POOKY IS A / ONE CAT / TEDDY BEAR

ANSWERS

The Great Anagram Scam

SUB	BUS	STUN	NUTS
MOPE	POEM	TEAMS	STEAM
SEAT	EAST	LAGER	REGAL
RATS	STAR	STEAL	LEAST

DANGER GARDEN

Garfield's Graffiti Game: JON 4 LIZ

Wit And Wisdom Word Search

(solution grid shown)

51

JON'S HAD LOTS OF NICE DATES - IN A BOX FROM THE SUPERMARKET!

**I LOVE MY TEDDY
AND MY TEDDY LOVES
ME!**

Nermal On Garfield
Garfield doesn't have a misspent youth — he was never young!

A Case of
MIDAS OVER MATTER

"Exciting news, Garfield!" cried Jon, bursting in through the front door.

"You've bought a tie that doesn't clash with your suit," suggested Garfield, hopefully.

"I've got a prezzie for you!" chuckled Jon.

"A bed with a built-in TV, fridge and coffeemaker," suggested Garfield, even more hopefully.

"It's something you've always needed," continued Jon, waving a bag in front of Garfield's face.

"An alarm clock with no hands and a silent bell," exclaimed Garfield, ecstatically.

"It could have been made especially for you . . ."

"Just gimme the thing!" interrupted Garfield, snatching the bag out of Jon's hand. "Guessing games are for dorks and dogs!" Garfield rummaged around inside the bag and held up a tin of pet food.

"MOGGYSLIM," he read, "a tasty and nutritious diet for cats who want to be a kitten again."

"It's a tasty and nutritious diet," said Jon, "for cats who are grossly overweight."

"That's not what it says on the label," snapped Garfield.

"Imagine, Garfield," exclaimed Jon, "you'll lose weight without feeling hungry! Aren't you pleased?"

"Thrilled!" said Garfield, tipping all the other tins onto Jon's foot.

And so the battle began! Jon gave Garfield nothing but the new cat food, and Garfield refused to eat it. Jon opened tin after tin, trying to tempt Garfield with the different flavours, but still Garfield refused to eat a single mouthful.

"This is the last tin," cried Jon, pushing a purple mixture towards Garfield. "Blueberry and blackcurrant surprise."

"You eat it," replied Garfield, pushing it back.

"I don't need to lose weight," said Jon.

"Neither do I," said Garfield.

In the end, Garfield grew so fed up that he told Odie to ring the front doorbell and run away. Jon went to answer the door and Garfield was waiting for him as he returned to the kitchen. SPLAT! Jon fell over Garfield and landed face-first in the slimming food.

"YEUCH!" spluttered Jon. "How DISGUSTING!"

"I rest my case," grinned Garfield

Garfield's trick only made Jon more determined to win this battle of wills.

"I'm removing every bit of proper food from the house," he said, carrying a box to the car.

"Couldn't you leave me a few scraps," begged Garfield," like the contents of the fridge-freezer?"

"I'm taking everything to Liz at the surgery," added Jon, passing by with another box. Garfield clung onto his leg.

"Take me with you," he pleaded. "I could eat her patients!"

His mouth set in a determined line, Jon drove off in a cloud of smoke. Garfield slouched back to his bed.

"I'll go to sleep for a month," he thought. "Jon will have changed his mind by then." This was easier said than done. Acute calorie-withdrawal kept Garfield awake. He tossed and turned in his little box, unable to find a comfortable position.

"I need something soothing," he muttered, "like a ten-course gourmet banquet."

Suddenly, as if by magic, a sunbeam appeared in a corner of the kitchen. It was the brightest, warmest and most inviting-looking sunbeam Garfield had ever seen in his life and it seemed to beckon him towards it. As if in a trance, Garfield crossed the floor and curled up in the soft yellow light with a contented sigh. Within seconds, he was fast asleep.

Garfield slept for about ten minutes. He woke up suddenly and felt strangely excited. There was something going on, but he did not know what it was. Garfield gave himself a kiss to make sure he was awake.

"Can't understand people who pinch themselves," he remarked. He was not dreaming, so he settled down to see what was going to happen. Nothing did!

"This is worse than waiting for the TV to warm up," he grumbled. In the end, Garfield decided to make his wait more comfortable by moving his bed into the sunbeam. But, the moment he touched the little box, it filled up with lasagne! Garfield's jaw dropped in total disbelief. Then, keeping it in the same wide-open position, he tipped the lasagne down his throat.

"Bit light on the mozzarella," he burped, "but otherwise delicious!"

After this unexpected feast, Garfield felt a bit thirsty. He spied a baking tin in the larder.

"I'll fill it with water," he thought.

But, as soon as he picked up the tin, it also filled with lasagne! This time, Garfield showed no surprise.

"I never met a lasagne I didn't like!" he chuckled, and swallowed the whole lot in a single gulp. "Hmm, extra garlic," he commented. "Perfect!"

By now, Garfield felt very thirsty. Setting his scruples aside, he picked up Odie's water bowl and drank it down. Instantly, the empty bowl filled up with lasagne.

"This is my ultimate fantasy come true!" exclaimed Garfield. "Everything I touch turns to lasagne!"

Garfield decided to make hay while the sun shone — or, rather, the sunbeam. He opened all the kitchen cupboards and touched every saucepan, dish, bowl and container that he could find. They all filled up with piping hot lasagne. Garfield scoffed the lot, and then touched the dishes again for seconds . . . and thirds . . . and fourths. Eventually, even Garfield could eat no more.

"But I'd better stock up for later," he cried.

Racing round the house, Garfield filled everything with lasagne.

"Jon *will* get a surprise when he puts on his bunny slippers," he giggled. Garfield ended up in the bathroom, touching the bathtub twice so that the lasagne rose right up to the ceiling.

"Better shut the door carefully," he giggled. "Don't want to get swept away in a lasagne-slide!"

After so much food and excitement, Garfield began to feel very tired. His bed still stood in the sunbeam and he stumbled towards it, rubbing his eyes.

"I should sleep for six months now," he yawned, contentedly.

Of course, the moment Garfield touched his bed, it filled with lasagne again. But Garfield was tired, he had gone into his eyes-closed-and-flop-into-bed routine. SPLAT! Garfield plunged face-first into a sea of sticky pasta.

"Pity it's not ravioli," he spluttered. "I'd be lying on little cushions."

Worse was to follow. Odie bounded in, holding a ball. Wagging his tail and barking excitedly, Odie threw the ball to Garfield.

"Sorry, Odie," cried Garfield, throwing the ball back, "I can't play right now."

The ball turned to lasagne in mid-air. FLUMP! It landed on Odie's head, covering him with rivers of thick tomato puree and gooey cheese sauce.

"Any other time, this would be funny!" groaned Garfield. Then Garfield noticed that his fur was matted with bits of food.

"I need a wash!" he said.

Garfield licked his paw and rubbed it round his ear. Instantly, his ear began to feel funny. He looked in the mirror.

"ARRGH!" he yelled. "Now *I'M* turning into lasagne!"

Garfield's ultimate fantasy had turned into a terrifying nightmare. He lay on the floor, scratching his pasta ear and wondering what to do.

"If I sit on Jon's lap," he wailed, "he'll turn to lasagne and there'll be nobody to look after me. If I kiss Arlene, she'll turn to lasagne and there'll be nobody to adore me. And if I kick Odie, there'll be nobody to insult — and, imagine, dog-shaped lasagne!"

A tear welled up in Garfield's eye and he rubbed it away with his paw. It was replaced by another made of melted cheese that ran slowly down his cheek and solidified on his nose.

Then, without warning, everything changed! The tear turned to water and splashed onto the ground. Garfield's ear became furry again. Odie's ball reappeared beside him and Garfield's bed emptied itself of lasagne.

"W-W-What's going on?" gasped Garfield.

Odie rolled his ball across the kitchen and Garfield noticed that the sunbeam in the corner had gone. Looking outside, he saw a big, black cloud had drifted across the sun.

"Stay there, please," pleaded Garfield, clasping his paws together. "Stay there and rain for the next six weeks!"

Odie gave a puzzled frown.

"You wouldn't understand, Odie," said Garfield, "but then that's nothing new."

A few minutes later, Jon came home.

"I'm sorry, Garfield," he cried, picking up his pet, "I think I've been a bit hard on you." Jon's back gave a sudden twinge and he dropped Garfield onto a chair.

"Gee-whiz, Garfield," he exclaimed, "I reckon you've tripled in weight since I saw you last!"

Garfield just curled up on the chair and closed his eyes.

"Don't go to sleep, Garfield," chuckled Jon, hurrying outside to the car, "I've got a surprise for you."

Jon returned carrying a huge lasagne.

"I had it specially made for you at the Italian restaurant in town," he said. "Let's forget your diet, eh? It only causes trouble between us."

Calmly and deliberately, Garfield took the lasagne from Jon, balanced it carefully in his right paw and threw it straight into Jon's face. Jon just stood there with the pie-dish stuck to his nose and food running down his neck.

"I'll never understand that cat!" he cried.

Garfield On Garfield

You can't improve on
perfection!